THE MUSIC OF GEORGE GERSHWIN FOR FLUTE

Arranged by Robin De Smet

WISE PUBLICATIONS
part of The Music Sales Group
London/New York/Paris/Sydney/Copenhagen/Berlin/Madrid/Tokyo

Published by
Wise Publications
14-15 Berners Street, London, W1T 3LJ, UK.

Exclusive Distributors:
Music Sales Limited
Distribution Centre, Newmarket Road, Bury St Edmunds,
Suffolk, IP33 3YB, UK.
Music Sales Pty Limited
20 Resolution Drive, Caringbah, NSW 2229, Australia.

Order No. AM68503
ISBN 978-0-7119-1333-2
This book © Copyright 2008 by Wise Publications,
a division of Music Sales Limited.

Unauthorised reproduction of any part of this publication by
any means including photocopying is an infringement of copyright.

Compiled and arranged by Robin De Smet.

Printed in the EU.

www.musicsales.com

Bess, You Is My Woman

Music by George Gershwin

© COPYRIGHT 1988 DORSEY BROTHERS MUSIC LIMITED, 8-9 FRITH STREET, LONDON W1V 5TZ. ALL RIGHTS RESERVED. INTERNATIONAL COPYRIGHT SECURED.

But Not For Me

Music by George Gershwin

©COPYRIGHT 1988 DORSEY BROTHERS MUSIC LIMITED, 8-9 FRITH STREET, LONDON W1V 5TZ. ALL RIGHTS RESERVED. INTERNATIONAL COPYRIGHT SECURED.

Embraceable You

Music by George Gershwin

© COPYRIGHT 1988 DORSEY BROTHERS MUSIC LIMITED, 8-9 FRITH STREET, LONDON W1V 5TZ. ALL RIGHTS RESERVED. INTERNATIONAL COPYRIGHT SECURED.

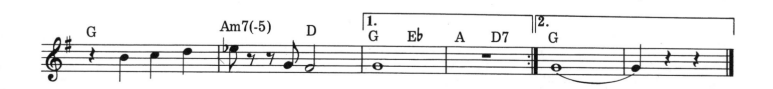

Fascinating Rhythm

Music by George Gershwin

© COPYRIGHT 1988 DORSEY BROTHERS MUSIC LIMITED, 8-9 FRITH STREET, LONDON W1V 5TZ. ALL RIGHTS RESERVED. INTERNATIONAL COPYRIGHT SECURED.

An American In Paris

Music by George Gershwin

© COPYRIGHT 1988 DORSEY BROTHERS MUSIC LIMITED, 8-9 FRITH STREET, LONDON W1V 5TZ. ALL RIGHTS RESERVED. INTERNATIONAL COPYRIGHT SECURED.

A Foggy Day

Music by George Gershwin

© COPYRIGHT 1988 DORSEY BROTHERS MUSIC LIMITED, 8-9 FRITH STREET, LONDON W1V 5TZ. ALL RIGHTS RESERVED. INTERNATIONAL COPYRIGHT SECURED.

How Long Has This Been Going On?

Music by George Gershwin

© COPYRIGHT 1988 DORSEY BROTHERS MUSIC LIMITED, 8-9 FRITH STREET, LONDON W1V 5TZ. ALL RIGHTS RESERVED. INTERNATIONAL COPYRIGHT SECURED.

I Got Plenty O' Nuttin'

Music by George Gershwin

© COPYRIGHT 1988 DORSEY BROTHERS MUSIC LIMITED, 8-9 FRITH STREET, LONDON W1V 5TZ. ALL RIGHTS RESERVED. INTERNATIONAL COPYRIGHT SECURED.

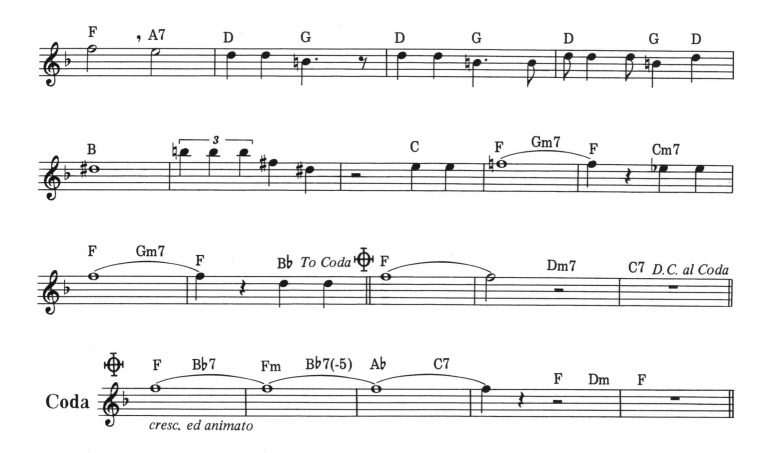

I Got Rhythm

Music by George Gershwin

© COPYRIGHT 1988 DORSEY BROTHERS MUSIC LIMITED, 8-9 FRITH STREET, LONDON W1V 5TZ. ALL RIGHTS RESERVED. INTERNATIONAL COPYRIGHT SECURED.

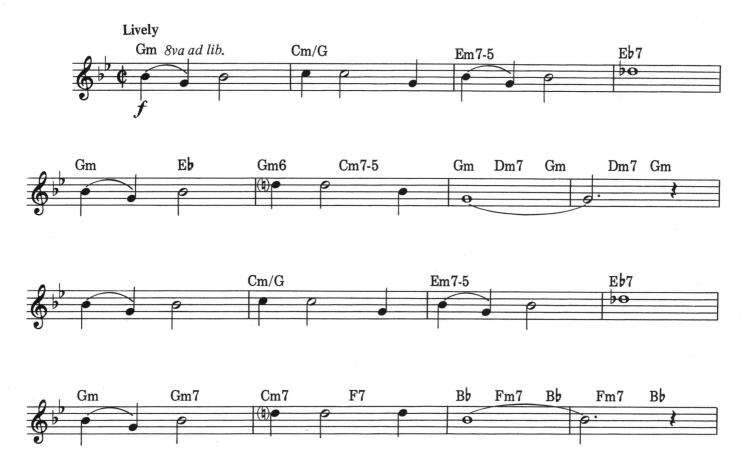

Rhapsody In Blue

Composed by George Gershwin

© COPYRIGHT 1988 DORSEY BROTHERS MUSIC LIMITED, 8-9 FRITH STREET, LONDON W1V 5TZ. ALL RIGHTS RESERVED. INTERNATIONAL COPYRIGHT SECURED.

I'll Build A Stairway To Paradise

Music by George Gershwin

© COPYRIGHT 1988 DORSEY BROTHERS MUSIC LIMITED, 8-9 FRITH STREET, LONDON W1V 5TZ. ALL RIGHTS RESERVED. INTERNATIONAL COPYRIGHT SECURED.

It Ain't Necessarily So

Music by George Gershwin

© COPYRIGHT 1988 DORSEY BROTHERS MUSIC LIMITED, 8-9 FRITH STREET, LONDON W1V 5TZ. ALL RIGHTS RESERVED. INTERNATIONAL COPYRIGHT SECURED.

Let's Call The Whole Thing Off

Music by George Gershwin

© COPYRIGHT 1988 DORSEY BROTHERS MUSIC LIMITED, 8-9 FRITH STREET, LONDON W1V 5TZ. ALL RIGHTS RESERVED. INTERNATIONAL COPYRIGHT SECURED.

The Man I Love

Music by George Gershwin

© COPYRIGHT 1988 DORSEY BROTHERS MUSIC LIMITED, 8-9 FRITH STREET, LONDON W1V 5TZ. ALL RIGHTS RESERVED. INTERNATIONAL COPYRIGHT SECURED.

Nice Work If You Can Get It

Music by George Gershwin

© COPYRIGHT 1988 DORSEY BROTHERS MUSIC LIMITED, 8-9 FRITH STREET, LONDON W1V 5TZ. ALL RIGHTS RESERVED. INTERNATIONAL COPYRIGHT SECURED.

Oh, Lady Be Good

Music by George Gershwin

© COPYRIGHT 1988 DORSEY BROTHERS MUSIC LIMITED, 8-9 FRITH STREET, LONDON W1V 5TZ. ALL RIGHTS RESERVED. INTERNATIONAL COPYRIGHT SECURED.

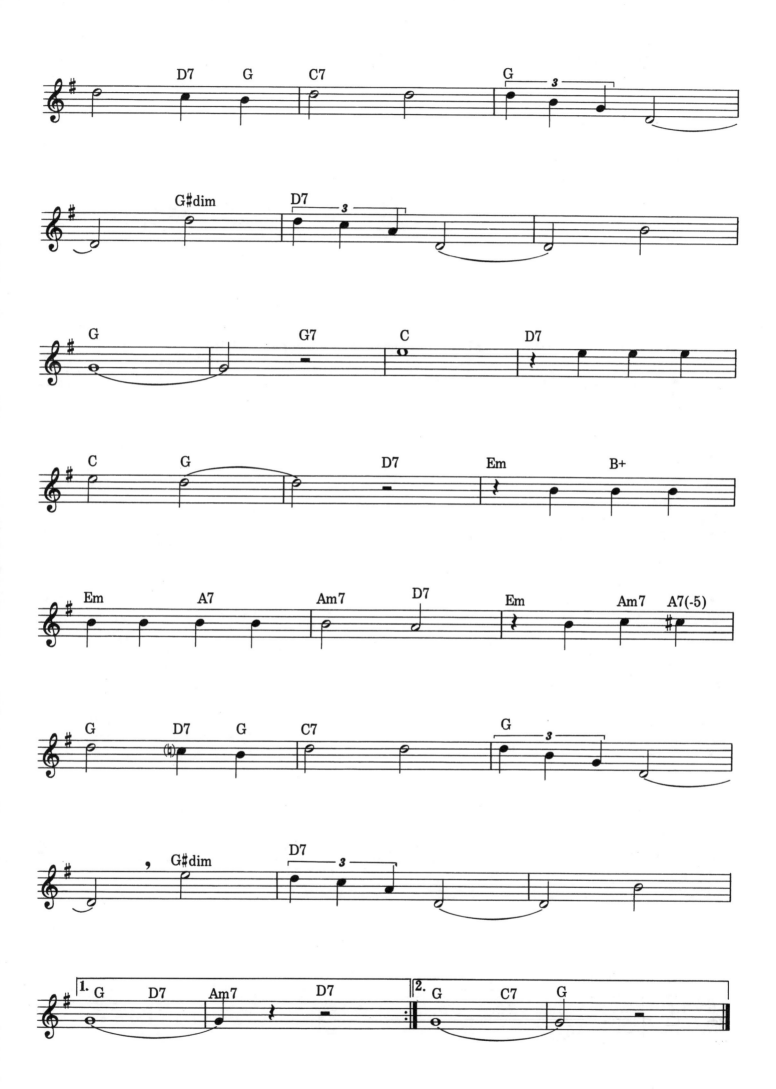

Somebody Loves Me

Music by George Gershwin

© COPYRIGHT 1988 DORSEY BROTHERS MUSIC LIMITED, 8-9 FRITH STREET, LONDON W1V 5TZ. ALL RIGHTS RESERVED. INTERNATIONAL COPYRIGHT SECURED.

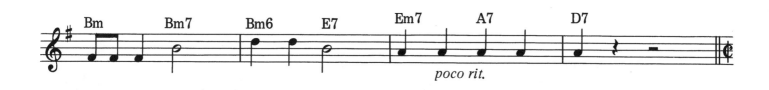

Someone To Watch Over Me

Music by George Gershwin

© COPYRIGHT 1988 DORSEY BROTHERS MUSIC LIMITED, 8-9 FRITH STREET, LONDON W1V 5TZ. ALL RIGHTS RESERVED. INTERNATIONAL COPYRIGHT SECURED.

Strike Up The Band

Music by George Gershwin

© COPYRIGHT 1988 DORSEY BROTHERS MUSIC LIMITED, 8-9 FRITH STREET, LONDON W1V 5TZ. ALL RIGHTS RESERVED. INTERNATIONAL COPYRIGHT SECURED.

Swanee

Music by George Gershwin

© COPYRIGHT 1988 DORSEY BROTHERS MUSIC LIMITED, 8-9 FRITH STREET, LONDON W1V 5TZ. ALL RIGHTS RESERVED. INTERNATIONAL COPYRIGHT SECURED.

's Wonderful

Music by George Gershwin

© COPYRIGHT 1988 DORSEY BROTHERS MUSIC LIMITED, 8-9 FRITH STREET, LONDON W1V 5TZ. ALL RIGHTS RESERVED. INTERNATIONAL COPYRIGHT SECURED.

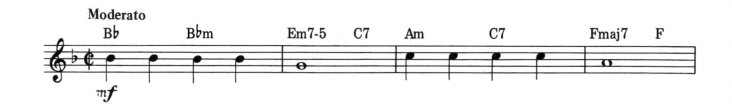

They All Laughed

Music by George Gershwin

© COPYRIGHT 1988 DORSEY BROTHERS MUSIC LIMITED, 8-9 FRITH STREET, LONDON W1V 5TZ. ALL RIGHTS RESERVED. INTERNATIONAL COPYRIGHT SECURED.

They Can't Take That Away From Me

Music by George Gershwin

© COPYRIGHT 1988 DORSEY BROTHERS MUSIC LIMITED, 8-9 FRITH STREET, LONDON W1V 5TZ. ALL RIGHTS RESERVED. INTERNATIONAL COPYRIGHT SECURED.

Summertime

Music by George Gershwin

© COPYRIGHT 1988 DORSEY BROTHERS MUSIC LIMITED, 8-9 FRITH STREET, LONDON W1V 5TZ. ALL RIGHTS RESERVED. INTERNATIONAL COPYRIGHT SECURED.

Bringing you the words and the music

All the latest music in print... rock & pop plus jazz, blues, country, classical and the best in West End show scores.

- Books to match your favourite CDs.

- Book-and-CD titles with high quality backing tracks for you to play along to. Now you can play guitar or piano with your favourite artist... or simply sing along!

- Audition songbooks with CD backing tracks for both male and female singers for all those with stars in their eyes.

- Can't read music? No problem, you can still play all the hits with our wide range of chord songbooks.

- Check out our range of instrumental tutorial titles, taking you from novice to expert in no time at all!

- Musical show scores include *The Phantom Of The Opera*, *Les Misérables*, *Mamma Mia* and many more hit productions.

- DVD master classes featuring the techniques of top artists.

Visit your local music shop or, in case of difficulty, contact the Marketing Department, Music Sales Limited, Newmarket Road, Bury St Edmunds, Suffolk, IP33 3YB, UK
marketing@musicsales.co.uk